FIRST GRADE

More Adventures of the SUPERKIDS

STUDENT BOOK  UNITS 5–6

Name

THE SUPERKIDS READING PROGRAM

More Adventures of the SUPERKIDS

BY PLEASANT T. ROWLAND

ILLUSTRATED BY LORETTA LUSTIG, MERYL HENDERSON & DOUG ROY

CONTRIBUTING WRITER: VALERIE TRIPP

DEVELOPED BY ROWLAND READING FOUNDATION

For the convenience of teachers and parents, this book contains abbreviated citations of the Common Core State Standards, noted in pink at the bottom of each page. The complete standards are available online at *superkidsreading.org*.

ISBN: 978-1-61436-227-2 MO36227.0315 2 3 4 5 6 4495 19 18 17 16 15

UNITS 1–2 3–4 5–6 7–8 9–10

ar

Unit 5

art jar yard dark farm smart

1. st__ __s 2. al__ __m 3. __ __m

4. g__ __den 5. d__ __ts 6. b__ __k

Parents: Your child underlined ar in the words at the top of the page, traced letters and wrote ar to complete the other words on the page, and then drew a line from each completed word to the part of the picture it names.

stars marbles shark jar
sharp park car card

1. P__k the ______.

2. The sh__k has ______ teeth.

3. The m__bles are in the ______.

4. Two st__s are on the ______.

Happy Birthday

Parents: Your child underlined *ar* in the words at the top of the page, used those words to complete the sentences below, and drew the missing parts of the pictures.

Parents: Your child underlined or in the words at the top of the page, traced letters and wrote or to complete the other words on the page, and then drew a line from each completed word to the part of the picture it names.

horn hard

1. Lily is working ______ on a puzzle.

pork park

2. The kids play at the ______.

cord card

3. Sal pulls the ______ on the lamp.

for far

4. Toc can run ______ without stopping.

storm star

5. The ______ kept the kids inside all day.

Parents: Your child chose and wrote words with *ar* or *or* to complete sentences about the pictures.

er ir ur

ladder	dirt	fur
monster	first	curl
person	thirsty	hurry

Parents: Your child underlined *er*, *ir*, and *ur* in the words at the top of the page and in the sentences below. Then your child followed the directions to mark the pictures.

1\.

Make her shirt purple.

2\.

Put an X on the dirty sneakers.

3\.

Draw a line under the third person.

4\.

Draw whiskers on the first cat.

5\.

Draw a river next to the church.

6\.

Put an X on the bird and the turtle.

Parents: Your child read the words at the top of the page and underlined *ir*, *er*, or *ur* in each word. Then your child matched words that have almost the same meanings, writing each word from the top of the page next to the matching word in the boxes.

chirp	stir	bother	burst
squirm	dirty	platter	burning

1. wiggle

2. tweet

3. flaming

4. disturb

5. plate

6. broke

7. mix

8. muddy

cold know does laugh both again

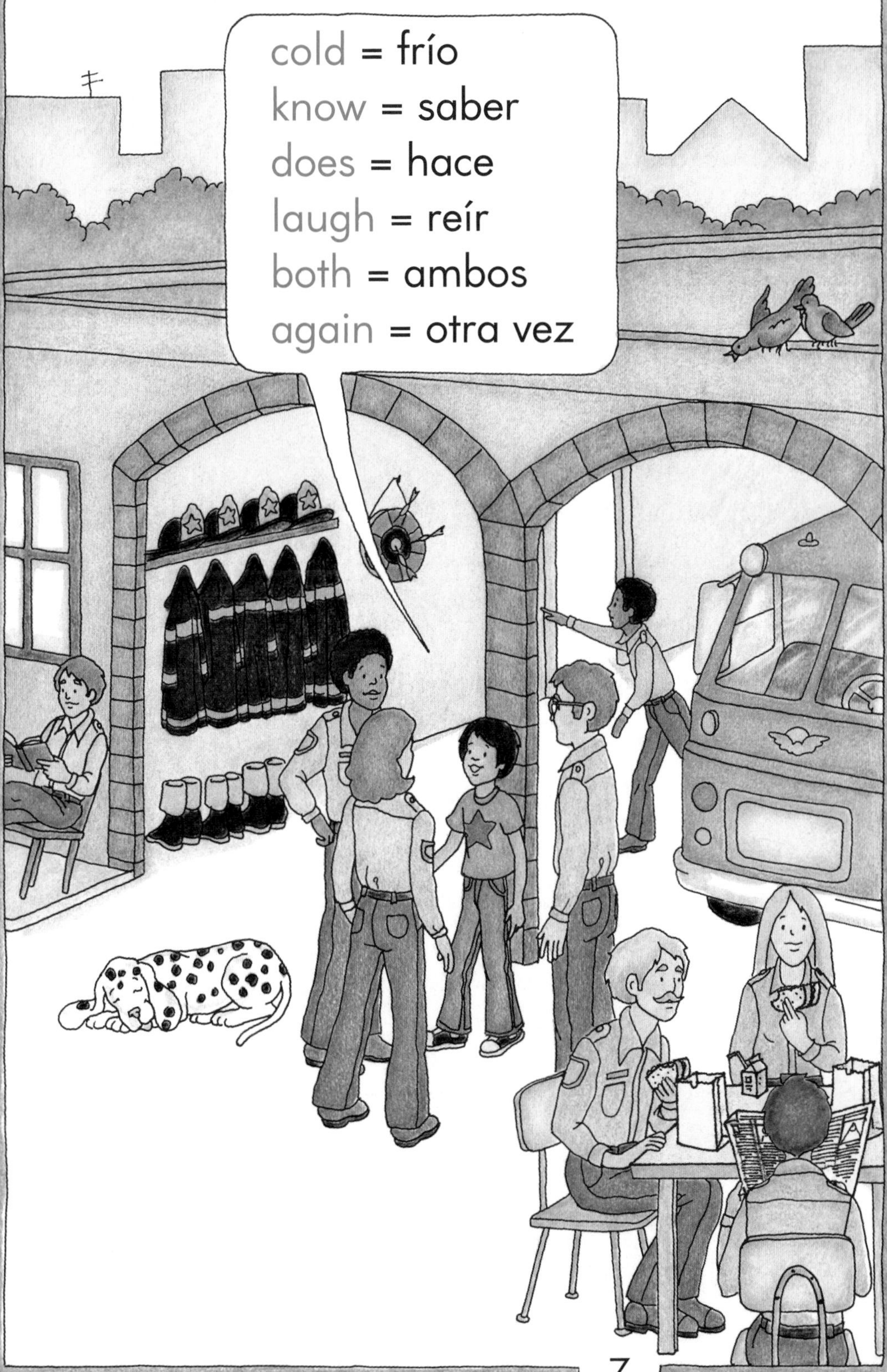
cold = frío
know = saber
does = hace
laugh = reír
both = ambos
again = otra vez

Parents: Your child listened to a CD, learned the pink Memory Words at the top of the page, and heard words in Spanish that have almost the same meanings as the Memory Words.

Vocabulary, Spelling
L.1.4, RF.1.3g, L.1.2d

Memory Words

cold

know

does

laugh

both

again

Parents: Help your child memorize the spelling of these Memory Words. Each word will be on the Unit 5 spelling test.

Pattern Words

ar

car
far
star

orn

born
corn

ern

fern
stern

ird

bird
third

urn

turn
burn

Parents: Help your child practice spelling words that follow patterns. Four of these words will be on the Unit 5 spelling test.

1. What could Sal do that helped the fire chief?
   - ○ put out a fire
   - ○ speak Spanish

2. Why did Carmen call the fire department?
   - ○ Her home was on fire.
   - ○ She wanted to visit the fire department.

3. Why did the firefighters hurry to the fire?
   - ○ to put the fire out before anyone got hurt
   - ○ to finish their work before lunch

4. Why was the Vargas family happy at the end?
   - ○ Their home did not catch on fire.
   - ○ Their family was safe.

5. What was the reporter's story about?
   - ○ two kids who helped save a family from a fire
   - ○ helpful tips to stop fires from starting

Parents: Your child answered questions about the story "Fire!" by filling in the bubble next to the correct answer for each question.

☆ MORNING STAR ☆

Sal and Carmen Help Fire Department 6

1. Yesterday Carmen Vargas called Fire Department 6.
2. She spoke Spanish and Chief Flinn could not understand her.
3. Purple cars are for sale this week.
4. Salvador Mirandez was visiting Fire Department 6.
5. Sal explained what Carmen was saying in Spanish.
6. Sal and the fire chief rushed to the fire.
7. Curt Hart is on a TV show called "The Lost Shark."
8. The firefighters saved the family and put out the fire.
9. A baby girl was born at the hospital yesterday.
10. The Vargas family thanked Chief Flinn after the fire was out.
11. The chief thanked Sal and Carmen for their help.

Parents: Your child drew lines through the sentences that do not tell how Sal and Carmen helped the fire department in the story "Fire!"

Parents: Your child traced and wrote Memory Words on cards, cut them out, and used them plus game pieces to play a game with the "board" shown on this page and page 11.

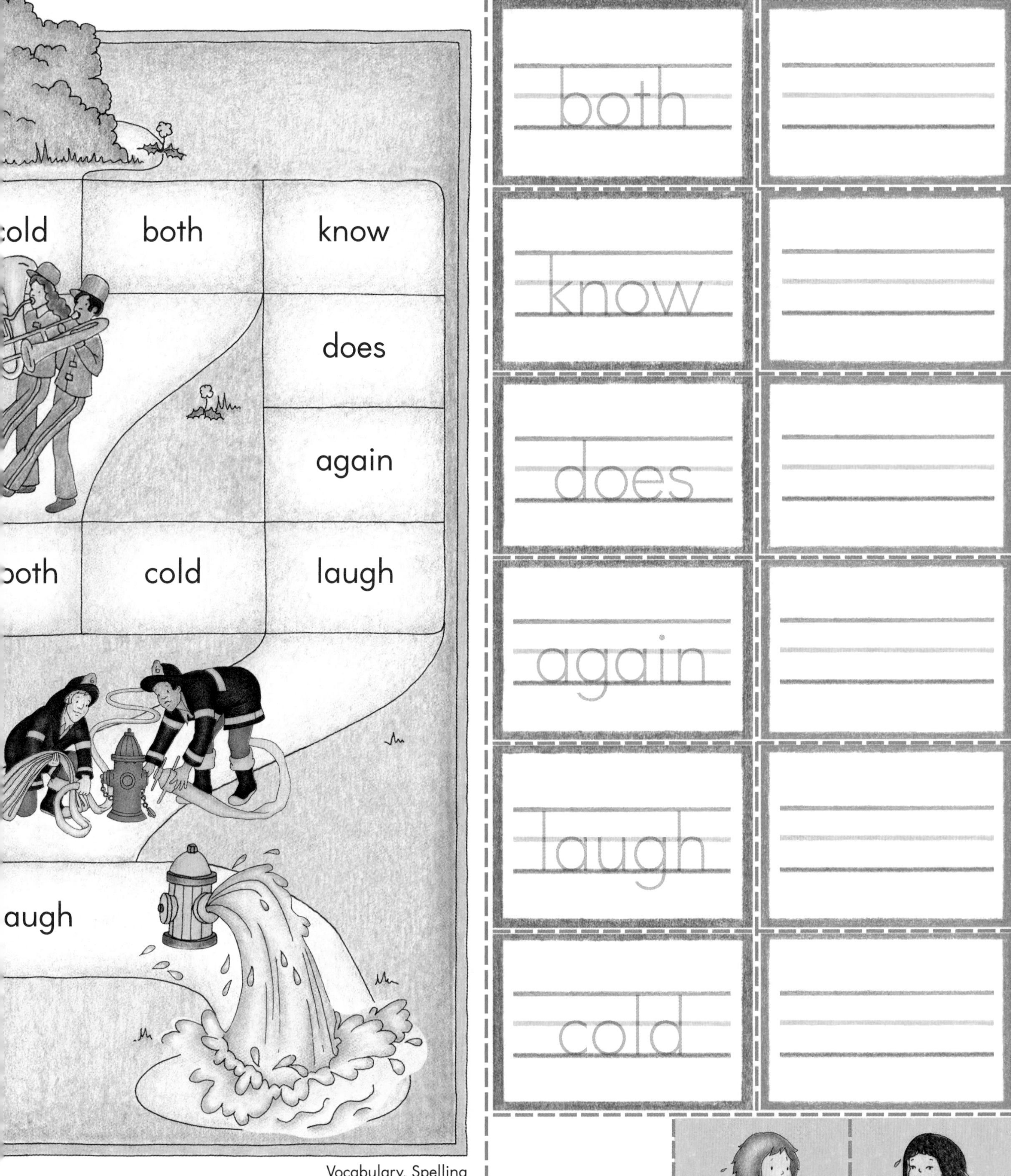

Vocabulary, Spelling
L.1.4, RF.1.3g, L.1.2d

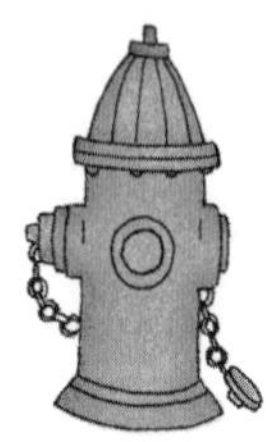

the bubble next to the word that tells how Icky was feeling when he said each group of words.

How did Icky feel when he said:

1. "Their hiding spots aren't as good as mine. Tic will never discover me."

   ○ pleased ○ angry

2. "Oh, no! Now I am stuck. I'll have to wait until the rain stops."

   ○ mean ○ upset

3. "Golly! You wet mutt! What are you doing here?"

   ○ surprised ○ bored

4. "But you and I can be brave together."

   ○ very afraid ○ less afraid

5. "I had the best hiding spot of all!"

   ○ happy ○ sad

1. Icky liked his hiding spot because

2. Icky stayed in the pipe because

3. Golly tried to sit on Icky's lap because

4. Icky petted Golly because Icky

5. Helping Golly made Icky feel

Parents: Your child completed sentences about the story "The Super Hiding Spot."

Comprehension
RL.1.1, L.1.1j

The ending ful can mean full of.

1. Icky gave Golly a lot of help during the storm.

He was 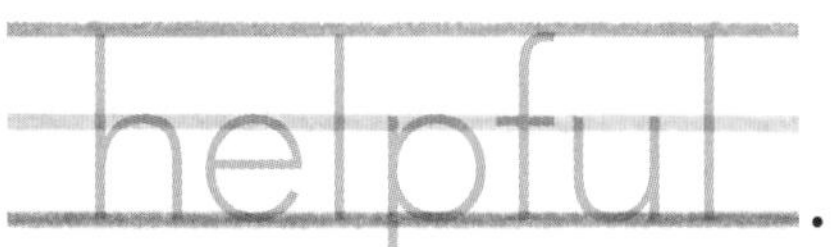.

2. Icky and Golly had hope that the rain would stop.

They were .

3. The rain stopped. Icky and Golly were thank______.

Parents: Your child traced and wrote letters to make words ending in *-ful.*

Unit 6

Parents: Your child underlined oi or oy in the words at the top of the page, traced a word with oi or oy in each box, and circled the picture that the word describes.

Phonemic Awareness, Phonics
RF.1.2c, RF.1.3

oi oy

Parents: Your child underlined *oi* and *oy* in words in the sentences on page 17 and then wrote the number of each sentence next to the person or animal in the picture on page 16 that the sentence describes.

1. She is using a sprinkler to make the dirt moist.

2. She has a small toy rake.

3. He was the first boy to plant his seeds so his plants are the tallest.

4. She is using a hoe to dig in the soil.

5. She is pointing down at her plants.

6. He is putting oil on the clippers.

7. He is enjoying the garden as he rests.

8. She has little foil packs of seeds.

9. He feels disappointed because his plants are small.

10. They are chirping a joyful song.

Pattern Words

oil

oil
boil
soil

oin

coin
join

oint

point
joint

oy

joy
toy

Parents: Help your child practice spelling words that follow patterns. Four of these words will be on the Unit 6 spelling test.

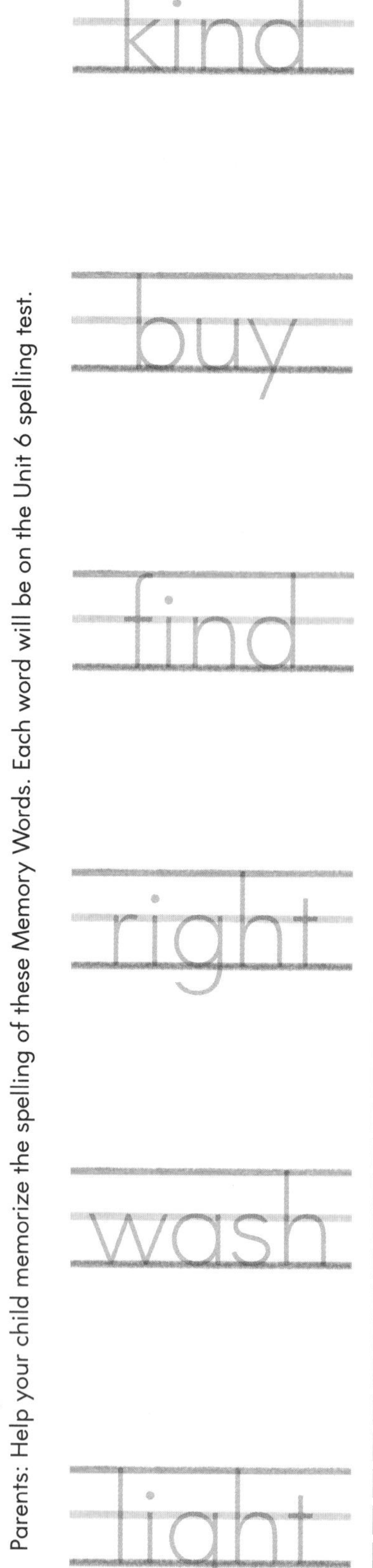

Unit 6, Lesson 266 (CD 1, Track 9)

kind buy find right wash light

No matter what kind
Of seeds you buy,
You will find
They will reach to the sky.
If you plant them right,
And the raindrops wash,
And the sun shines light,
Up they will pop, by gosh!

Tac

Tic

Parents: Your child listened to a song on CD and read the lyrics on the page to learn the Memory Words in pink.

Vocabulary, Spelling
RF.1.3g, L.1.4, L.1.2d

1. 

Toc and Alf waited in line.

2. 

The Superkids forgot to buy seeds for Toc and Alf.

3. 

Alf and Toc planted the birdseed.

4. 

Toc and Alf kept the soil moist.

Toc and Alf got birdseed.

The gardener gave Toc and Alf plot number 4.

The birdseed plants got bigger and blossomed.

The Superkids made fun of Toc and Alf.

Parents: The sentences in the boxes tell about events from the story "For the Birds." Your child drew arrows from the boxes on the left to the boxes on the right to show which event on the left caused the event on the right to happen.

Parents: Your child traced the blue letters and wrote *oi* or *oy* to complete words that describe the pictures.

RF.1.3g, L.1.2d

to make a book. Then your child wrote Memory Words on the lines as instructed.

The End

5. Put the seed pack on a stick. Then you can remember what kind of seeds you planted.

How to Plant Carrots

2. Find a good spot for the garden.

1. Go to the store and buy seeds.

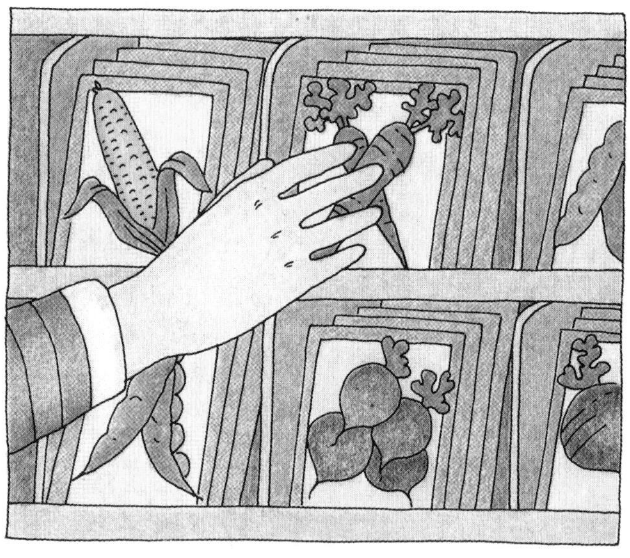

6. When the green part is tall, it is time to dig up the carrots. Wash them off. Then eat them up.

3. Plant the seeds where it's sunny. The plants will need lots of light.

4. Sprinkle the seeds with a hose right away.

The ending ly can tell you how a person did something.

1.

What did Cass do softly?

2.

What did Sal do quickly?

3.

What did Toc do neatly?

4.

What did Frits do sadly?

5.

What did Tic do happily?

6.

What did Icky do cheerfully?

Parents: Your child underlined the ending *-ly* in the pink words and then circled the picture that answered each question.

Parents: Your child answered questions about the story "The Lost Mitt" by filling in the bubble next to the correct answer for each question.

1. Why did Frits lend Ettabetta his mitt?
   - ○ His mitt was new.
   - ○ His mitt was better than her mitt.
   - ○ She needed it for the big game.

2. Why was Ettabetta happy at the end of the game?
   - ○ She made a fantastic catch and her team won.
   - ○ She hit the ball far.
   - ○ She gave Frits a new mitt.

3. What did Ettabetta do with Frits's mitt?
   - ○ She kept it.
   - ○ She left it at the park.
   - ○ She gave it back to Frits.

4. What was Ettabetta's plan?
   - ○ to buy Frits a new mitt
   - ○ to ask Icky for help
   - ○ to lend Frits her mitt

5. Why was Ettabetta happy at the end of the story?
   - ○ Her team won the game.
   - ○ She and Frits both had mitts.
   - ○ Frits gave her a bat.

Comprehension
RL.1.1, RL.1.10, SL.1.1

How would Ettabetta say it?

1\. sadly thankfully

"Frits, your mitt was fantastic," she said ____________________.

2\. softly sleepily

"I must catch that ball," she whispered ____________________.

3\. happily sadly

"That was the best game," she said ____________________.

4\. sadly cheerfully

"Oh, Frits will be so mad," she said ____________________.

5\. hopefully sleepily

"Maybe I can make some cash," she said ____________________.

Parents: Your child completed sentences by choosing and writing words ending with *-ly* that tell how Ettabetta in the story "The Lost Mitt" would have said the words in quotation marks.

Comprehension; Vocabulary; Grammar, Usage, and Mechanics
RL.1.3, RL.1.9, L.1.4a, RF.1.4c, L.1.4b, L.1.1

1. “Get it! Get the ball, Ettabetta,” the kids said noisily.

- ○ whispered
- ○ hollered
- ○ mumbled

2. “Oh, no! Frits will be mad at me,” Ettabetta said sadly.

- ○ chuckled
- ○ sang
- ○ groaned

3. “We won! We won the game,” the kids said joyfully.

- ○ mumbled
- ○ groaned
- ○ cheered

4. “What did I do with the mitt?” Ettabetta said softly.

- ○ whispered
- ○ yelled
- ○ called

Parents: Your child read each sentence and then filled in the bubble next to the word that has almost the same meaning as the pink words in the sentence.

right light kind buy wash find

1. Turn on the light. / kind.

2. I can't find / right my lost mitten.

3. I need to light / wash the muddy car.

4. Raise your right / wash hand.

5. Helping a pal is buy. / kind.

1.

3.

Parents: Your child chose and circled a Memory Word to complete each sentence and wrote that word in the puzzle. Then your child drew pictures for sentences 1 and 3.

Vocabulary, Spelling
RF.1.3g, L.1.4, L.1.2d

right kind light

1. The man was very good to the kids.

Do you like this sort of fruit?

2. Turn on the lamp.

This box is easy to lift.

3. What you said is correct.

Turn this way. It's not left.

Parents: Your child read a pair of sentences and then wrote on the lines the Memory Word from the top of the page that has almost the same meaning as the pink words in both sentences.

Parents: Your child wrote sentences to answer questions about things he or she can do.

1. What can you do quickly?

2. What can you do happily?

3. What can you do carefully?

4. What can you do sloppily?

5. What can you do softly?

6. What can you do easily?

Parents: Your child found, traced, and circled spelling words from Units 5 and 6 to complete the puzzle.

ISBN 978-1-61436-227-2
90000
9 781614 362272